C000050645

Granny's Book

Granny's Book

A scrapbook for memories

JUDY ROSE

Copyright © Judy Rose 2011

The right of Judy Rose to be identified as the author of this
work has been asserted by her in accordance with the
Copyright, Designs and Patents Act 1988.

This edition first published in Great Britain in 2011 by
Orion Books
an imprint of the Orion Publishing Group Ltd
Orion House, 5 Upper St Martin's Lane,
London WC2H 9EA
An Hachette UK Company

1 3 5 7 9 10 8 6 4 2

All rights reserved. Apart from any use permitted under UK copyright law,
this publication may only be reproduced, stored or transmitted, in any form,
or by any means, with prior permission in writing of the publishers or,
in the case of reprographic production, in accordance with the terms of
licences issued by the Copyright Licensing Agency.

A CIP catalogue record for this book is available
from the British Library.

ISBN: 978 1 4091 3251 6 (hardback)

Printed and bound in Spain

The Orion Publishing Group's policy is to use papers that are natural,
renewable and recyclable and made from wood grown in sustainable forests.
The logging and manufacturing processes are expected to conform to the
environmental regulations of the country of origin.

Every effort has been made to fulfil requirements with regard to
reproducing copyright material. The author and publisher will be glad
to rectify any omissions at the earliest opportunity.

www.orionbooks.co.uk

Contents

Introduction

GRANNIES have always held a special place in our hearts and in our lives for the powerful bond that exists between them and their grandchildren can form the basis of one of the most loving, meaningful and rewarding relationships we can have. I recall my own grannies with deep love and affection; they were both plump and jolly figures usually inhabiting their natural territory – the kitchen. In both their homes I would often sit and watch while they produced a wonderful array of home-cooked food that I would be offered, fresh from the oven. Looking back though, I wish I had spent more time asking them questions about how life was for them when they were growing up. With the arrogance of youth, I think that I considered them to be positively ancient when they were only in their sixties!

Now that I'm seeing life from the other side of the table, as a granny myself, I have experienced the intense joy that my grandchildren have brought. In this book, your granny can preserve for eternity her wonderful tales, happy memories, hand-me-down recipes and photographs in one special place, ensuring that while photos fade, memories stay bright.

JUDY ROSE, mother of three, granny of two

All about me

What is your full name?

_____

What do you know about your birth?
When and where were you born?

_____

_____

_____

What was going on in the world when you were born?

Here's some space for photos of you,
young and old . . .

What does being a mum and a granny mean to you?

Grandmas are mums with lots of frosting.

~ANON

What makes you laugh?

And what makes you cry?

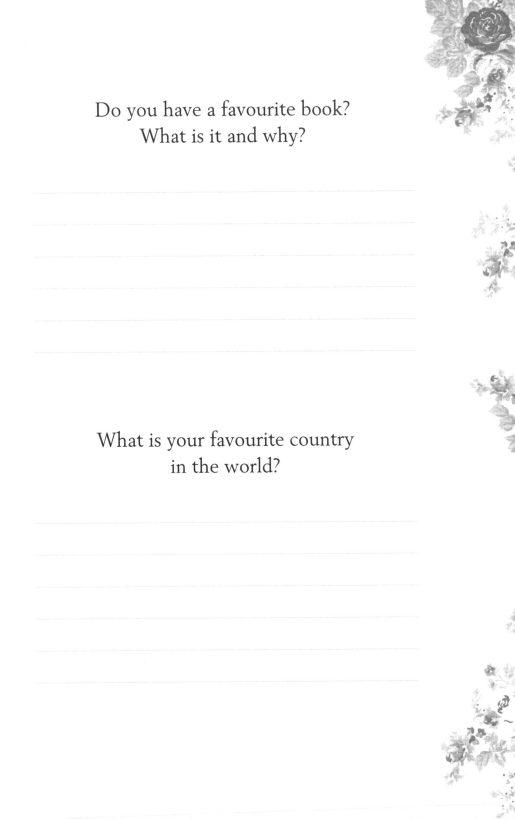

Do you have a favourite book?
What is it and why?

What is your favourite country
in the world?

If you could pick anywhere in the world to go for a holiday, where would it be and why?

Your favourite holiday . . .

What five things would you take to a
desert island for a week, and why?

_The best place to be when you're sad,
is at your granny's side._

~ANON

Is there something you have always
wanted to do, but haven't?

Tell us one thing about you that we
don't already know

My family

Can you describe in three words
what family means to you?

What can you remember about your
grandparents on your mum's and
your dad's side?

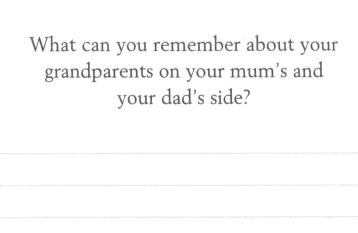

_____

_____

_____

_____

_____

Did you see them often? Do you wish
you'd seen them more?

_____

_____

_____

_____

Do you know about when and where they were born? Were any of them born and brought up outside the UK? If so, why do you think they came here?

Grandmothers are just antique little girls.

~ANON

Do you know how either set
of your grandparents met?

Can you recall any stories they told you
about their lives?

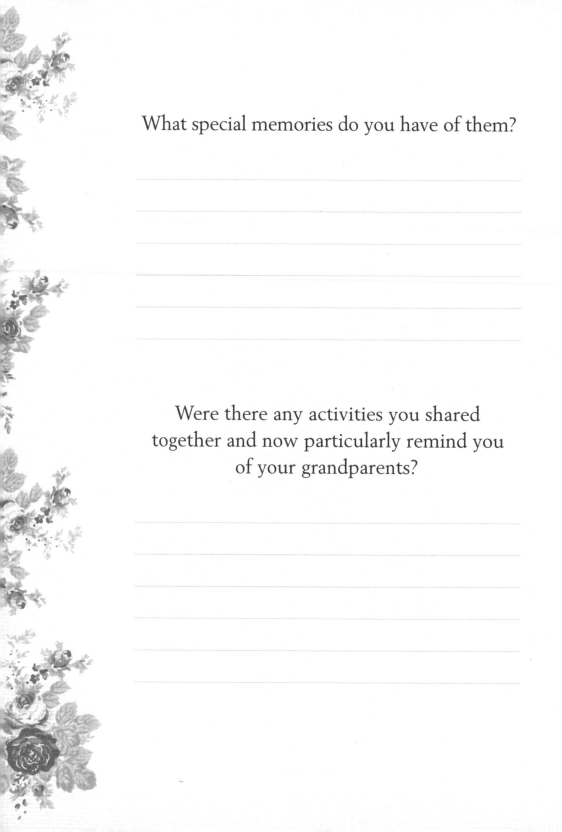

What special memories do you have of them?

Were there any activities you shared
together and now particularly remind you
of your grandparents?

Can you see any of their personalities
reflected in you?

Tell us about your parents. What were their names and when were they born?

Perfect love sometimes does not come until the first grandchild.

~WELSH PROVERB

What do you know about their childhoods?

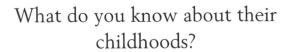

Were they naughty at school or top
of the class?

Did they tell you any stories about their
lives when they were young?

Do you know how your parents met?
Was it love at first sight?

What do you know about their wedding?

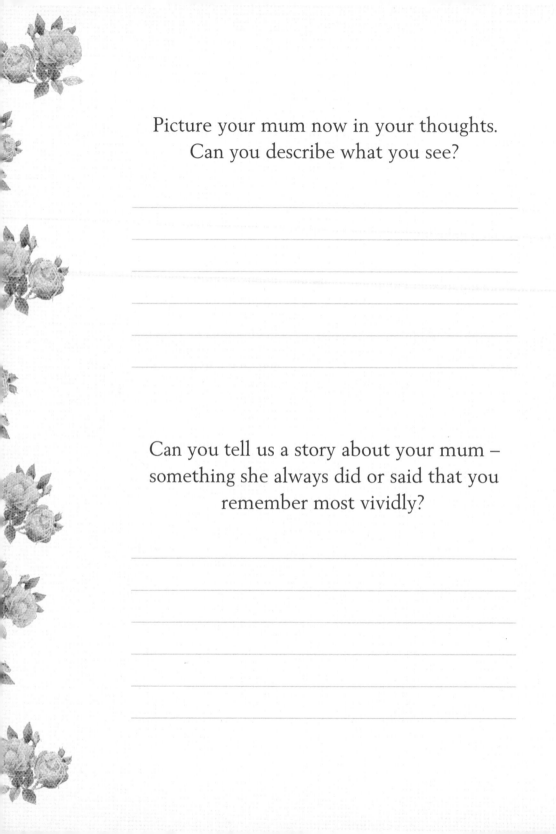

Picture your mum now in your thoughts.
Can you describe what you see?

_____

_____

_____

_____

_____

Can you tell us a story about your mum –
something she always did or said that you
remember most vividly?

_____

_____

_____

_____

_____

What three words would you use to
describe your mum?

_____

_____

_____

Is there one piece of advice that your
mum gave you that you will never forget?
What was it?

_____

_____

_____

_____

_____

_____

_____

Do you have a favourite meal that your
mum used to cook for the family? What was
it and can you share the recipe here?

Do you think you've inherited any
of your mum's characteristics?

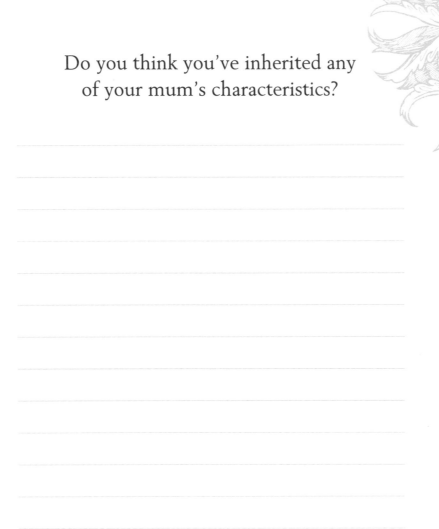

*A grandparent is old on the outside but
young on the inside.*

~ANON

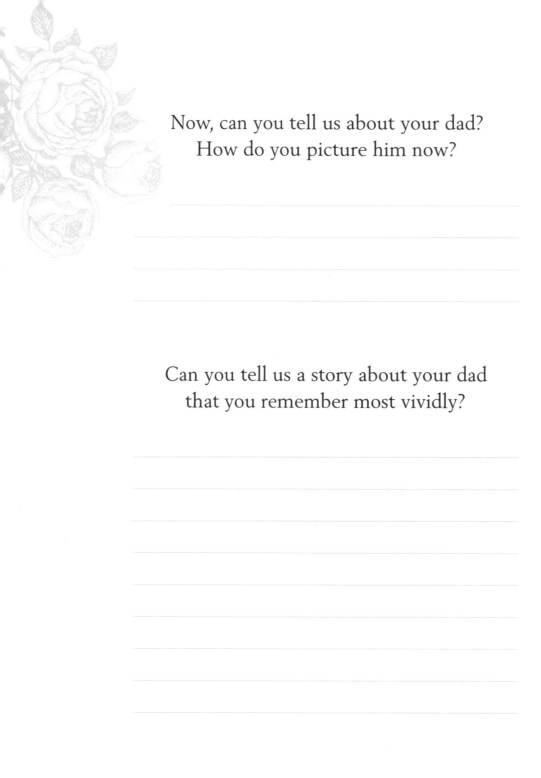

Now, can you tell us about your dad?
How do you picture him now?

_____

_____

_____

_____

Can you tell us a story about your dad
that you remember most vividly?

_____

_____

_____

_____

_____

_____

_____

_____

What did your dad do for a living?

Which of your dad's characteristics
do you think you have inherited?

What about brothers and sisters?

What are their names and are they older
or younger than you?

Were you close to your brothers and sisters?

Were there any games you used to
play together?

Your brothers, sisters and cousins . . .

As you grew up, did your relationships with
your brothers and sisters change?

_____

_____

_____

Did you have any family nicknames?
What were they and why?

_____

_____

_____

Is there one member of your family who
you feel had a particular influence on you?
Who was it and why?

_____

_____

Your family tree

Use this space to trace your family
so we can see where you fit in.

My earliest memories

What is your earliest memory? How old were you and what was going on?

_____

_____

_____

_____

_____

_____

Some pictures of you . . .

How would you describe yourself as a child?

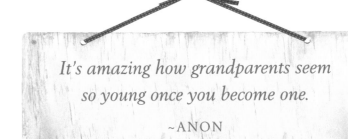

*It's amazing how grandparents seem
so young once you become one.*

~ANON

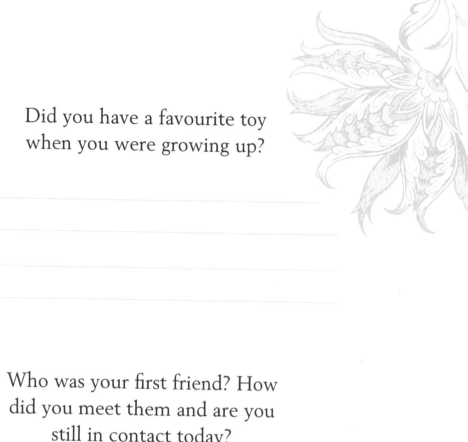

Did you have a favourite toy
when you were growing up?

Who was your first friend? How
did you meet them and are you
still in contact today?

Tell us about the friends you made at primary school. What were their names and what did you do together?

There's no place like home except Grandma's.

~ANON

Here is some space for photos of your friends . . .

Did your family have any family traditions, at Christmas for example?

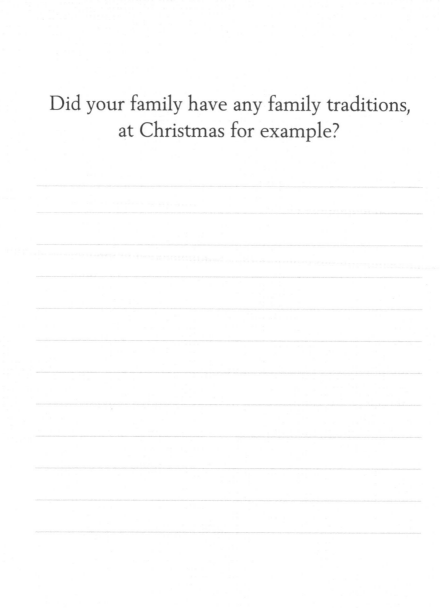

Uncles and aunts, and cousins, are all very well,
and fathers and mothers are not to be despised; but
a grandmother, at holiday time, is worth them all.

~FANNY FERN

What was your first family house like?
Can you describe your bedroom?

_____

_____

_____

_____

Have you been back to visit your house
since? How has it changed?

_____

_____

_____

_____

_____

_____

Do you remember your
first pet?

Granny's heart is a patchwork of love.

~ANON

What was the first single you bought?

And do you remember the first film you
saw at the cinema?

Growing up

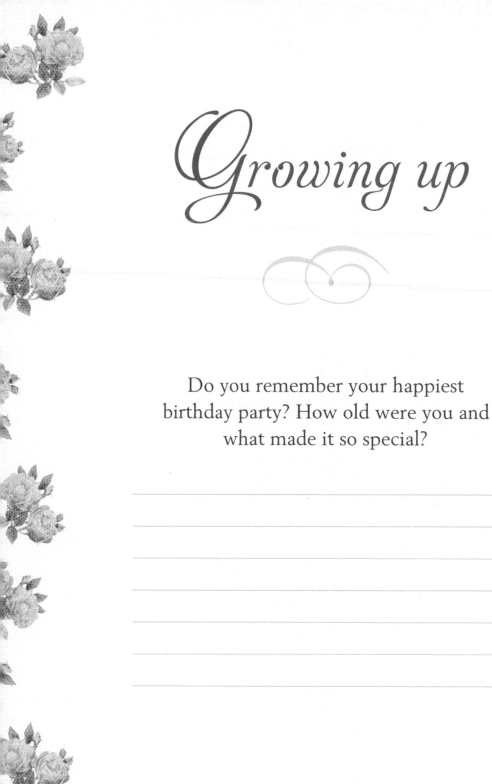

Do you remember your happiest
birthday party? How old were you and
what made it so special?

_____

_____

_____

_____

_____

_____

What was the best holiday you went on with your family?

_____

_____

_____

_____

_____

_____

_____

_____

_____

_____

A house needs a grandma in it.

~LOUISA MAY ALCOTT

Your holidays . . .

Share one of your favourite memories
of your teenage years

If you visualise yourself as a teenager now,
what would you be doing?

_It's one of nature's ways that we often feel closer
to distant generations than to the generation
immediately preceding us._

~IGOR STRAVINSKY

Did you enjoy school? Did you have a
favourite subject? And what about a worst?

Is there one teacher who stands out?
Who was it and why were they special?

What was the naughtiest thing you ever did at school?

Being grandparents sufficiently removes us from the responsibilities so that we can be friends.

~ALLAN FROME

What made you laugh when
you knew you shouldn't?

_____

_____

_____

_____

Were you sporty? If so, were you in
any school teams?

_____

_____

_____

_____

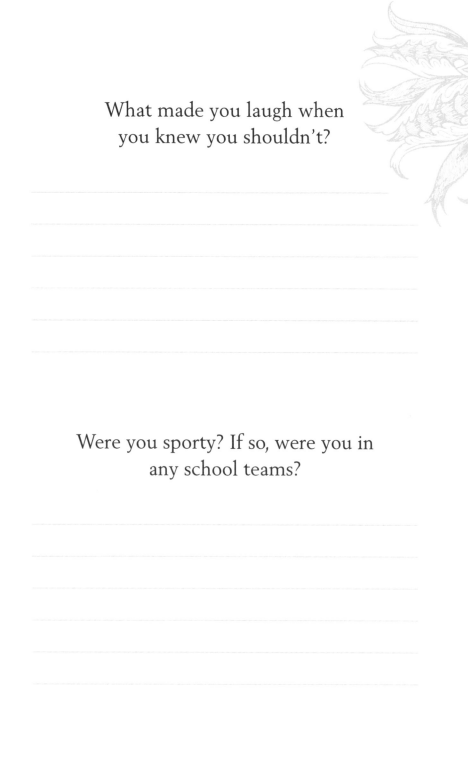

How would you describe yourself as a child?

Did you have any hobbies while you were at school?

What did you do after you left school?
Did you go to university?

If you went to university, tell us about it.
Where did you go and what did you study?

When a child is born, so are grandmothers.

~ANON

Did you have a classic dish you made
at university? What was it and can you
share the recipe?

When did you leave home? Did you miss it?

Did you have a favourite book that you
would read again and again?

And if you had to pick three songs that
remind you of your childhood which ones
would they be and why?

Did you have a crush on a celebrity like an
actor or a musician? Who was it and why?

What is your happiest memory from
your childhood?

_____

_____

_____

_____

_____

And your saddest?

_____

_____

_____

_____

When you were young, what dreams
did you have about what you
wanted to be when you grew up?

The world of work

What was your job? Where did you
work and who with?

Did you enjoy your first job?

_____

_____

_____

_____

_____

_____

_____

_____

_____

_____

_____

_____

_____

Grandmas never run out of hugs or cookies.

~ANON

Are you a spender or a saver?

Was there one special thing that
you saved up for?

What, in life, have you found
the most rewarding?

Is there anyone you have met through work
who has had a big influence on your life?
Who and why?

Do you think your attitude towards work
has changed over the years?

_____

_____

_____

_____

_____

_____

_____

_____

_____

_____

Granny – a wonderful mum
with lots of practice.

~ANON

Did you find it difficult balancing your work life with your family life?

_____

_____

_____

_____

What advice can you give us about the world of work?

_____

_____

_____

_____

What would your dream job be and why?

My friends

What qualities do you look for in
a friend?

_____

_____

_____

_____

_____

_____

_____

_____

Have those qualities changed as you've changed?

_____

_____

_____

_____

_____

_____

_____

_____

_____

_____

They say genes skip generations.
Maybe that's why grandparents find their
grandchildren so likeable.

~JOAN MCINTOSH

Who were your best friends at school –
primary and secondary? What were their
names and what were they like?

Are you in touch with any of your
school friends today?

If you went to university which
friends did you make there?

When you were younger, what was your
favourite night out with your friends?
Were you a party animal or did you prefer
a quiet night in?

And what about now? What do you
like to do with friends?
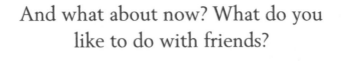

Can you share a story that brings back
happy memories of time you have spent
with your friends?

What's the nicest thing one of your friends
has done for you?

My loves

Who was your first date and
where did you go?

_____

_____

_____

_____

_____

_____

_____

Tell us about your first kiss

_It is as grandmothers that our mothers
come into the fullness of their grace._

~CHRISTOPHER MORLEY

Tell us about your first true love. How did you meet them and what were they like?

Have you ever had your heart broken?
How did you cope?

_____

_____

_____

_____

What is the most romantic thing anyone
has ever done for you?

_____

_____

_____

_____

_____

_____

_____

When and where did you meet grandad?

Tell us about the first time you met
grandad's parents

_____

_____

_____

_____

Can you remember what grandad looked
like when you first met?

_____

_____

_____

_____

_____

_____

_____

What was it about him that first attracted you to him?

Grandchildren are compensation for growing old.

~ANON

What special characteristics
does he have?

What kind of things did you do together
when you first met?

Did you have a special song that was 'yours'?

_____

_____

_____

_____

Were you ever separated for a long
period of time and, if so, how did this
affect your relationship?

_____

_____

_____

_____

_____

_____

_____

Tell us how you got engaged. Was it romantic?
How long after you met did you get engaged?

What was your wedding like, where
was it and who did you invite?

Who were the bridesmaids?
And who was the best man?

Can you describe your first
home together?

What was the most difficult thing to
adjust to in married life?

What is the best thing about
being married?

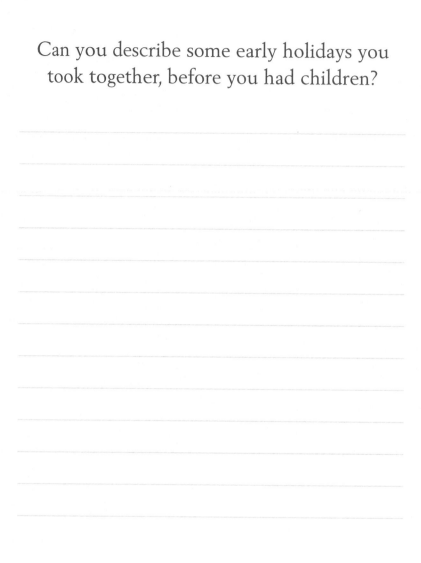

Can you describe some early holidays you
took together, before you had children?

Grandmother-grandchild relationships are simple.
Grandmas are short on criticism and long on love.

~ANON

In what ways did marriage turn out to be different to what you expected?

What would you say is the most important
thing about choosing a partner for life?

What advice would you give me
on my wedding day?

And what about married life?
What wisdom can you share?

A family of my own

When you first found out you were
pregnant, how did you feel?
Were you nervous?

What about grandad? How did he feel?

_____

_____

_____

_____

_____

Did you and grandad know how many
children you wanted?

_____

_____

_____

_____

_____

How old were you both?

Did you agree on names before your children
were born? If so, did you stick to them?

What were the first few weeks of
motherhood like?

What did you find harder than
you expected?

How did it change your life?

Once you had a family of your own, did
the way you feel about your parents and
siblings change?

Did your parents enjoy becoming
grandparents?

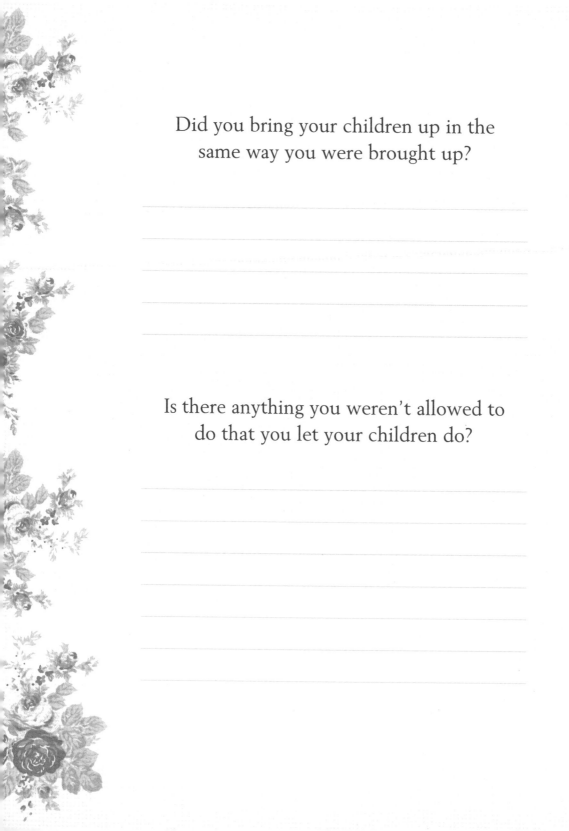

Did you bring your children up in the
same way you were brought up?

Is there anything you weren't allowed to
do that you let your children do?

What do you think had the greatest
influence on your children's personalities,
nature or nurture?

Did your children get on together when
they were young?

_____

_____

_____

_____

Do you remember what games they used
to play together?

_____

_____

_____

_____

_____

_____

Can you share any homemade remedies that have been passed down the generations, for treating a cold, for example?

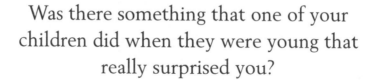

Was there something that one of your
children did when they were young that
really surprised you?

What is the funniest or most embarrassing
thing you remember any of them doing?

Do you have any particularly special
memories of your children growing up?

How did you feel when they left home?

Grandma's kitchen ... kids eat free.

~ANON

What matters to me

Have your values changed as you've
got older and wiser?

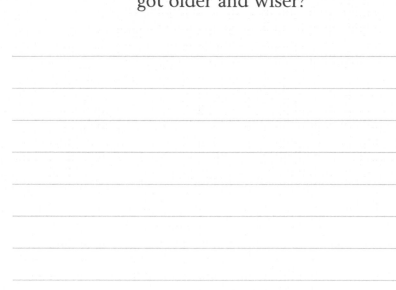

Do you have a favourite poem?
Can you share it here?

What have been the hardest choices you
have had to make during your life?

What was the best decision you ever made?

Who in life do you most
admire and why?

Can you remember someone saying
something to you that had a big impact
on how you lived your life?

Is there one event that you can pinpoint
that caused your life to take a totally
unexpected turn?

Is there one particular cause that you
feel passionate about?

*A grandmother is a mother who has
had a second chance.*

~ANON

Do you believe in God, or do you have
any other religious belief?

_____

_____

_____

_____

_____

How do you feel this has influenced the
way you live your life?

_____

_____

_____

_____

_____

Do you believe in life after death?

A garden of love grows in a
grandmother's heart.

~ANON

What have you done in life that you are
particularly proud of?

If you had a dinner party and you could
invite three other people – past and present
– who would they be and why?

_____

_____

_____

_____

_____

_____

_____

_____

_____

And what would you eat? Can you share
the recipes for your perfect meal
on the opposite page?

My wisdom for you

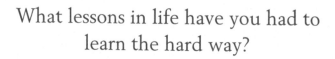

What lessons in life have you had to
learn the hard way?

_____

_____

_____

_____

_____

_____

_____

_____

What personal beliefs would you like
to pass on to your family?

Do you have a motto in life?

If nothing is going well, call your grandmother.

~ITALIAN PROVERB

What advice can you give about relationships and love?

When life is tough, what helps keep you positive?

Is there something specific you think about
that comforts you?

Is there one thing that you think
everyone should see or experience?

On this final page, if you had to give
one piece of wise advice what would
it be and why?

This special book opens you up to your loved ones, uncovering all those things that make you unique, and gives you the opportunity to relive all those happy memories as you and your family live, laugh and grow together. This is a family heirloom in the making.